DEVELOPING **MATHEMATICS**

**Customisable
teaching resources
for mathematics**

USING AND APPLYING MATHEMATICS

Ages 4–5

**Hilary Koll
and Steve Mills**

A & C Black • London

Contents

Talk about, recognise and recreate simple patterns

Describe solutions to practical problems, drawing on experience, talking about their own ideas, methods and choices

Published 2009 by A & C Black Publishers Limited
36 Soho Square, London W1D 3QY
www.acblack.com

ISBN 978-1-4081-1314-1

Copyright text © Hilary Koll and Steve Mills 2009
Copyright illustrations © Jenny Tulip 2009
Copyright cover illustration © Piers Baker 2009
Editor: Marie Lister
Designed by Billin Design Solutions Ltd

The authors and publishers would like to thank Catherine Yemm and Judith Wells for their advice in producing this series of books.

A CIP catalogue record for this book is available from the British Library.

Printed and bound in Great Britain by Halstan Printing Group.

A&C Black uses paper produced with elemental chlorine-free pulp, harvested from managed sustainable forests.

Introduction

100% New Developing Mathematics: Using and Applying Mathematics is a series of seven photocopiable activity books for children aged 4 to 11, designed to be used during the daily maths lesson. The books focus on the skills and concepts for Using and Applying Mathematics as outlined in the Primary National Strategy *Primary Framework for literacy and mathematics*. The activities are intended to be used in the time allocated to pupil activities in the daily maths lesson. They aim to reinforce the knowledge and develop the skills and understanding explored during the main part of the lesson, and to provide practice and consolidation of the learning objectives contained in the Framework document.

Using and Applying Mathematics

There are several different components which make up the **content** of maths and form the bulk of any maths curriculum:

- **mathematical facts**, for example a triangle has three sides;
- **mathematical skills**, such as counting;
- **mathematical concepts**, like place value.

For maths teaching to be successful, it is vital that children can use this mathematical content beyond their classroom, either in real-life situations or as a basis for further understanding. However, in order to do so they require extra abilities over and above the mathematical content they have learned. These extra abilities are often referred to as the **processes** of mathematical activity. It is these processes which make mathematical content usable.

As an example, consider this question:

How many triangles are there in this shape?

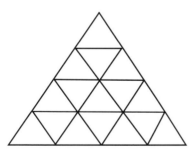

The mathematical 'content' required is only:

- the **fact** that a triangle has three sides
- the **skill** of counting

As such, it could be expected that very young children could solve this problem. The fact that they cannot suggests that other abilities are involved. These are the processes, and for this question they include:

- visualising the different-sized triangles;
- being systematic in counting all the triangles of different sizes;

- looking for patterns in the numbers of triangles;
- trial and error;
- recording.

Unless children can apply these processes in this situation, then however good their counting skills and knowledge of triangles may be, they will fail.

The strand 'Using and applying mathematics' of the *Primary Framework for mathematics* emphasises the importance of using and talking about mathematics in real situations. This series of books is intended to make more explicit the processes involved in learning how to put one's maths to use.

Using and Applying Mathematics Ages 4–5 supports the development of the using and applying processes by providing a series of activities that provide opportunities to introduce and practise them through a series of activities. On the whole the activities are designed for children to work on independently, although due to the young age of the children, the teacher may need to read the instructions with them and ensure that they understand the activity before they begin working on it.

Pre-school, children are naturally inquisitive about the world around them. They like to explore and experiment, and to make marks and record things on paper in their own idiosyncratic ways. Unfortunately, once at school, the focus is often placed firmly on the maths 'content' alone and children can be led to believe that maths is not a subject of exploration, but rather one of simply learning the 'right way to do things'. As a result, when older children are asked to explore and investigate maths they are often at a loss if their maths teaching to date has not encouraged and built upon their natural instincts.

Ages 4–5 helps children to develop the following processes:

- predicting
- visualising
- looking for pattern
- recording
- reasoning
- making decisions
- estimating
- explaining
- being systematic
- co-operating
- comparing
- testing ideas
- trial and improvement
- asking own question

When using these activities, the focus need not be on the actual mathematical 'content'. Instead, the teacher's demonstrations, discussions and questioning should emphasise the processes the children are using. When appropriate, invite the children to explain their thinking to others. Research has shown that children develop processes most successfully when the teacher encourages pupils to act as experts rather than novices, granting them more autonomy, and encouraging a range of approaches to any problem rather than constraining discussion to produce an overall class plan. The children should evaluate their own plans against other plans in the posing, planning and monitoring phases of the lessons.

Ages 4–5 helps children to develop the skills of Problem-solving, Reasoning and Numeracy (PSRN) recommended by the Early Years Foundation Stage (EYFS) through stories, songs, games and imaginative play. To give all children the best opportunities for effective mathematical development, practitioners should give particular attention to:

- many different activities, some of which will focus on mathematical development and some of which will draw out the mathematical learning in other activities, including observing numbers and patterns in the environment and in daily routines;

- practical activities underpinned by children's developing communication skills;

- activities that are imaginative and enjoyable;

- real-life problems, for example: 'How many spoons do we need for everyone in this group to have one? ';

- modelling mathematical vocabulary during the daily routines and throughout practitioner-led activities;

- giving children sufficient time, space and encouragement to use 'new' words and mathematical ideas, concepts and language during child-initiated activities in their own play;

- encouraging children to explore problems, to make patterns and to count and match together;

- the balance between learning and teaching indoors and outdoors (e.g. having read a story about washing clothes, there might be laundrette play indoors and washing line play outdoors; streets of clothes shops built out of recyclables; bikes and other wheeled vehicles being used as delivery vans; numbered (and lettered) parking spaces. The staff would spend time in both environments and the level of child-initiated and practitioner-led activity would be monitored and divided more or less equally across both environments. Displays would include examples from both environments).

Ages 4–5 also helps children with Solving Problems, Representing, Enquiring, Reasoning and Communicating, as recommended in the revised Primary Framework. These five themes, although identified separately in the table below, are interlinked.

Solving problems	Representing	Enquiring	Reasoning	Communicating
Use developing mathematical ideas and methods to solve practical problems	Match sets of objects to numerals that represent the number of objects	Sort objects, making choices and justifying decisions	Talk about, recognise and recreate simple patterns	Describe solutions to practical problems, drawing on experience, talking about their own ideas, methods and choices

Extension

Many of the activity sheets end with a challenge (**Now try this!**), which reinforces and extends children's learning, and provides the teacher with an opportunity for assessment. Again, it may be necessary to read the instructions with the children before they begin the activity. For some of the challenges the children will need to record their answers on a separate piece of paper.

Organisation

Very little equipment is needed, but it will be useful to have available: coloured pencils, counters, cubes, scissors, glue, coins, plastic shapes such as Logiblocks and fruit, squared paper, number lines, grids and tracks.

Where possible, the children's work should be supported by ICT equipment, such as number lines and tracks on interactive whiteboards, or computer software for comparing and ordering numbers. It is also vital that children's experiences are introduced in real-life contexts and through practical activities. The teachers' notes at the foot of each page and the more detailed notes on pages 6 to 13 suggest ways in which this can be done effectively.

To help teachers select appropriate learning experiences for the children, the activities are grouped into sections within the book. However, the activities are not expected to be used in this order unless stated otherwise. The sheets are intended to support, rather than direct, the teacher's planning.

Some activities can be made easier or more challenging by masking or substituting numbers. You may wish to re-use pages by copying them onto card and laminating them.

Accompanying CD

The enclosed CD-ROM contains all of the activity sheets from the book and a program that allows you to edit them for printing or saving. This means that modifications can be made to further differentiate the activities to suit individual pupils' needs. See page 14 for further details

Teachers' notes

Brief notes are provided at the foot of each page, giving ideas and suggestions for maximising the effectiveness of the activity sheets. These can be masked before copying.

Further explanations of the activities can be found on pages 6 to 13, together with examples of questions that you can ask.

Whole class warm-up activities

The following activities provide some practical ideas that can be used to introduce or reinforce the main teaching part of the lesson, or provide an interesting basis for discussion.

Imagine my shape

Describe a flat shape that you have hidden and ask the children to guess what shape it is, for example 'Ouch, ouch, ouch…The shape has 3 corners. It has 3 straight sides. What do you think it looks like?'. Give a child a shape, secretly and ask them to describe it to others in the class for them to guess what it is.

How many ways?

Hold up 3 coloured cubes, for example red, blue and yellow. Ask the children to suggest different ways that you could put them in a line (red, yellow, blue; blue, red, yellow etc). Record the children's suggestions and encourage them to find all six ways that they can be arranged. A variation on this is to ask three children to stand in a line and to record all the different ways they can stand.

Number relationships

Encourage the children to guess the number you are thinking of giving clues such as:

The number comes before nine.
The number comes after five.
It is three more than four.
It is three less than ten.
It is an odd number

Once the children have played the game several times they can choose their own numbers to give clues about.

How many?

Hold some cubes in your hand and show them to the children. 'How many cubes do you think I have in my hand?' Discuss estimates and then count to check. Invite several children to grab a handful of cubes themselves and estimate who has most. Children then count to check.

Notes on the activities

Use developing mathematical ideas and methods to solve practical problems

This aspect of Using and Applying Mathematics deals with Solving Problems. It is central to all mathematics and if the children are unable to solve problems then the mathematics that they know is wasted. The children need to develop confidence in tackling problems without looking to teachers or other children for help. They should learn to decide which facts are key to the problem, make decisions about what operations to use and then follow them through, checking to see if their answer is a sensible one.

Picnic planning: 1 and 2 (pages 15–16)

Processes: recording, making decisions, reasoning

An important part of early problem-solving and numeracy work comes from seeing and using numbers in real situations. These sheets could be used as a follow on from some practical play using plates, cups and cutlery etc. It could also be linked to stories about bears and the teddy bears' picnic. Encourage the children to make sure that there are enough items for each bear and to record the information in a way that will help them to remember in the future.

SUGGESTED QUESTIONS:
* Has each bear got the same things?
* Can any of the bears share this item?
* How many of these do you think should be taken?
* What food are you taking that would mean you needed to take these bowls?

Sammy: 1 and 2 (pages 17–18)

Processes: testing ideas, visualise, trial and improvement, being systematic

In these activities the children must move the starfish around and put him in different positions on the grid. They should be encouraged to notice that sometimes he is touching fish (and/or crabs) and sometimes he is not. They should then try to find specific positions to match the given rules. Encourage the children to visualise and try out ideas and draw attention to those who use a systematic approach. Point out that there can be more than one solution for each. Finally, the children could stick the fish onto their sheet in a particular position and these could be displayed, describing how many starfish (and/or crabs) he is touching each time.

SUGGESTED QUESTIONS:
* Can you see any positions where you think Sammy will touch 1 fish? 2 fish? 3 fish?
* Put him there now. Were you correct?
* Are there any other places you could put him that would mean he was touching the same number of fish?
* Who is Sammy touching?

Wonderful wellies (page 19)

Processes: predicting, estimating, visualising, comparing, testing ideas

This activity could follow on from some practical work with boots or shoes in the cloakroom. Encourage the children to predict whether there are enough boots for the number of feet. They can talk to a friend about this, before counting to check. Some children might find it easier to count using a cube on each boot or foot and moving them away as they are counted. The children could also draw a line from a boot to a foot and then work out how many boots are left, if any.

SUGGESTED QUESTIONS:
* Do you think there are enough boots? Are there too many feet or too many boots?
* How many feet did you count?
* If there are not enough boots, how many more do you need?
* How many 'pairs' of boots are there?

Who sees who? (page 20)

Processes: visualising, reasoning, explaining

This activity gives the children an opportunity to visualise things from another's perspective. It can also reinforce positional words such as 'between', 'next to', 'opposite' etc.

SUGGESTED QUESTIONS:
* Is there a wall between the frog and the mouse?
* How many creatures can the worm see?
* Can the caterpillar see the worm?
* Who can the spider see?
* I want to draw a beetle somewhere on this map so that it can see the spider and the worm. Where could I draw it?

Wacky wigs: 1 and 2 (pages 21–22)

Processes: being systematic, making decisions, comparing, trial and improvement

This activity encourages the children to begin the process of working systematically, which takes most children many years to develop fully. Wacky wigs: 1 involves ensuring that no two style of wigs are the same colour, using only red, green and blue colours and that each wig is only coloured in one colour. Wacky Wigs: 2 involves colouring each wig in two colours, each half a different colour, and again ensuring no two are alike. For the second activity, discuss that the left half might be blue and the right half green as being different from a wig where the right half is blue and the left half green,

SUGGESTED QUESTIONS:
* How many wigs have you coloured blue? blue and green?
* Can you think of another way that you could colour the wig using red and green?
* Are any of the wigs you have coloured the same?
* How did you decide what to colour next?

Colourful cotton reels (page 23)

Processes: being systematic, making decisions, comparing, looking for pattern, recording

This activity continues with the idea of working systematically, in order to find different possibilities. Children should initially work practically with 3 colours of coloured cotton reels to make different towers like those shown. They should then be given coloured pencils in three colours and asked to record the different towers they have made. Some children may require more than one sheet to record their answers. Collectively, the different ways found by the whole class could be shown and the children encouraged to continue to find new ones.

SUGGESTED QUESTIONS:

• How many different towers have you made?
• Have you recorded them all? Can you think of another way that you could colour the tower?
• Are any of these towers the same?
  What is different about these two towers?

Rug rats (page 24)

Processes: visualising, making decisions, reasoning, being systematic, testing ideas

Children will need counters for these activities. Provide them with the sheet and ask them to pick some counters and place them on the rugs. Ask them to say how many on one rug first and then say how many on the other rug. Explain that those counters in the central section are actually on top of both rugs. Once the children have understood this concept they can attempt the problem-solving activity, trying to place counters in such a way that the number on each rug is the same. Draw attention to those children who try a systematic approach and explain that many different solutions are possible. These answers are examples of how 4 counters could be placed on each rug:

SUGGESTED QUESTIONS:

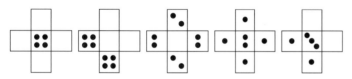

• How did you find this solution?
• Can you find a way if you use 5 counters? 4 counters? 6 counters?

Hide the buns: 1 and 2 (pages 25–26)

Processes: visualising, making decisions, reasoning, being systematic, testing ideas

Children will need counters for these activities. Provide them with the sheet and ask them to cover one of the buns with a counter. Initially ask them to say how many buns they can see in each row. Then ask them to say how many they can see in each column, demonstrating the meaning of the word column to the class. Once the children have understood this concept they can attempt the problem-solving activities, trying to place counters in such a way that the number in each row and column is the same.

SUGGESTED QUESTIONS:

• How did you find this solution?
• Have you checked each row and column?
• If you were to do this again, would you try a different way?

Match sets of objects to numerals that represent the number of objects

The next theme of the Framework's Using and Applying strand deals with Representing. It focuses on the children making sense of a problem or puzzle and organising the information in a way that enables them to solve it. In the early years, children may rely on practical materials and diagrams but as they develop confidence in this area may move on to using numbers, calculations and other modelling, including tables, lists or even the use of algebra.

Record on the clipboard (page 27)

Processes: recording, comparing

The focus of this activity should be on allowing the children to develop their own ways of recording. Each child will have a different view on how to show this information on paper. Some may try pictorial representations, others may use shapes or their own form of tallies, others may draw upon their knowledge of counting and figures when recording. It is vital that all types of recording are valued and that the children have opportunities to explain their markings to others. Compare the different types of recordings and invite the children to say which type they find easiest to understand.

On a table or in a particular area of the classroom lay out a number of the items shown. More confident children could have an area with more of the items.

Once the children have recorded the items, draw attention to the different ways that they have done this, for example tallies, drawings, numerals. Ask the children to compare them and to say which methods they think are the clearest and easiest to understand. Children could also, at a later date, be given a completed sheet and asked to collect together that number of items and place them on the table.

SUGGESTED QUESTIONS:

• Look, Claire has decided to draw the things but Sam has written the number. These are both clear ways of showing the information. Which do you prefer? Why?
• Tell us about your chart. How would you do it next time?

How many? 1 and 2 (pages 28–29)

Processes: estimating, explaining comparing, asking own questions

This activity can be used to encourage the children to compare and count children in the picture and to ask their own questions about what the children are doing. Page 29 can be used with children who are confident in counting and writing numerals. The cards can be cut out and ordered. As an extension activity, the children could make their own cards showing children doing other activities to compare and order.

SUGGESTED QUESTIONS:

• Are there more children skipping than playing in the sand tray?
• Are there fewer children looking at a book than are drawing?
• Which is the largest group of children? What are they doing?

Cube trail: 1 and 2 (pages 30–31)

Processes: comparing, looking for pattern, co-operating

These cards could be laminated and cut out to be used as a more permanent resource. Encourage the children to work in pairs to complete the number line and to place the correct number of multilink cubes on the squares. Children who are not fully able to recognise numerals to 10 are assisted by the pieces joining together in only one way.

SUGGESTED QUESTIONS:

- How many more cubes are here than here?
- Which number comes next?
- What card is this? How many cubes does it show?

The zoo (page 32)

Processes: estimating, testing ideas

This activity can be used as an assessment to see how well the children can match sets of objects to the numerals that show how many. Children can talk about the pictures and ask their own questions, such as 'Which type of animal is there most of?' 'How many more lions are there than penguins.'

SUGGESTED QUESTIONS:

- Which type of animal is there most of – tigers or lions?
- How many more/fewer tigers are there than…?
- How many more giraffes have you drawn?
- Can you draw 4 chimps? 3 zebras? etc.

Number puzzle (page 33)

Processes: looking for pattern, visualising

These cards could be laminated and cut out to be used as a more permanent resource. Encourage the children to work in pairs to complete the number puzzle. Once completed, the children can describe what they see and collect groups of objects to match each numeral.

SUGGESTED QUESTIONS:

- What do you notice about these shapes?
- How did you decide where to put each piece?
- Can you find me some cubes to match this number?

Money magician (page 34)

Processes: looking for pattern, recording, reasoning, explaining

Encourage the children to count the number of coins in both hands in each pair and to say any patterns they notice. Look at a number line and ask them to find the numbers on it, i.e. the even numbers. Ask the children to say whether it is possible to have an odd number of coins, if the same number is in each hand.

SUGGESTED QUESTIONS:

- What if you had one coin in each hand?'
- What if you had 2 coins in each hand?
- Can you find these numbers on a number line?

Flower bugs (page 35)

Processes: testing ideas, visualise, trial and improvement, being systematic

In these activities the children must move around the cards showing half flowers so that they create a sequence of whole flowers with 1, 2, 3, 4, 5 and 6 bugs on respectively. Encourage children to visualise and try out ideas and draw attention to those who use a systematic approach. Finally, the children could stick the flowers onto paper and could write the correct numeral under each flower which can then be displayed.

SUGGESTED QUESTIONS:

- How many bugs on this flower?
- Why did you decide to put that there?
- Can you tell me the order of the flowers?

Fishy friends (page 36)

Processes: comparing, reasoning

Before copying the sheet, the numeral could be changed to provide a more flexible set of resources. Here children are asked to draw fish to make up the total given by the numeral. Encourage discussion of each tank and for children to explain how many more they have drawn to develop early addition or subtraction vocabulary.

SUGGESTED QUESTIONS:

- How many fish do you think there is in Christopher's tank? Shall we count them?
- How many more fish have you drawn here?
- How could we explain to someone how many there are?
- One fish and then four more fish makes five fish. Can you explain this tank in the same way?

Underwater friends (page 37)

Processes: comparing, reasoning

This similar activity can be used in the same way. Before copying, the numeral could be changed to provide a more flexible set of resources. Again, encourage discussion of the creatures on each rock and ask the children to explain how many more they have drawn to develop early addition or subtraction vocabulary.

SUGGESTED QUESTIONS:

- How many creatures have you drawn here?
- How could we explain to someone how many there are?
- Can you tell me about the creatures on the rock using the words 'more than' or 'less than'?

Sort objects, making choices and justifying decisions

This theme encourages the children to pursue lines of enquiry. Initially, children learn to ask questions and go on to develop skills of planning, organisation and decision-making. The children need to be taught how to use pictures, lists and diagrams when organising information and supporting their line of enquiry.

Families (page 38)

Processes: looking for pattern, reasoning, making decisions, explaining, cooperating

Young children naturally look for patterns and should be encouraged to explain their reasons for sorting to other children and adults. For this activity, encourage the children to sort not just into pictures of the same thing, but to think about whether there is an alternative way of sorting, such as grouping those items related to the numbers 2, 3 or 4. As an extension activity ask them to draw further cards to add to the sets. The importance of this activity is in children being able to explain the features and their reasons for sorting in their particular way. Also, in working with a partner, co-operation skills can be explored.

SUGGESTED QUESTIONS:

• Can you explain to us about your groups?
• Why did you put this card here?
• Did anyone else sort theirs in a similar way?
• How many cards have you in this group?

Talking signs (page 39)

Processes: reasoning, explaining, co-operating, making decisions

There are no right or wrong ways of sorting these signs. Some children may collect together signs that look like letters, those that look like numbers or signs, those that are shapes and those that are 'squiggles' whilst others may use other criteria that is personal to them. The importance of this activity is in children being able to explain the features and their reasons for sorting in their particular way. Also, in working with a partner, co-operation skills can be explored. Note that it can be useful to have a spare set of signs for when children become fixed on a sign being in two sets.

This can produce valuable discussions. Ask each pair to explain their sorting to the others in the class and discuss differences between the pairs' ideas. If children have stuck the cards on different sheets of paper, these cane form a useful display and provoke further discussion.

SUGGESTED QUESTIONS:

• Can you explain to us about your groups?
• Why did you put this sign here?
• Did anyone else sort theirs in a similar way?
• How many signs have you in this group?
• Adults use this sign when doing maths (*, +, - or =). Does anyone know what it means?

Picture passports (page 40)

Processes: co-operating, reasoning, being systematic

Organise the children into groups of six, ideally all seated around a table so that they can see each other. Encourage them to make a card for each person, including themselves. Allow children to spend time working out whether they have drawn each person and discuss those who chose to be systematic, for example by working around the table or starting with the boys etc. Once completed, these cards can be used in a variety of ways (ideas below) and the cards could be laminated for longevity.

When the children arrive in the classroom they can put their own card in a particular place or hand it to the teacher so that the cards themselves, rather than the children can be counted to see who is here. This personal registration is a valuable way of children appreciating that representations can be used to count rather than items themselves.

The cards for a group of children could be placed face down and one selected for a particular task.

Pictures of absent children could be posted on the board each day.

Children volunteering for an activity could give their own picture to the teacher or place in a special place.

Classroom organisation can involve the cards, for example the cards of those doing a particular activity could be stuck on the wall in a group and children find themselves and work out what they should be doing,

SUGGESTED QUESTIONS:

• How are you sure that you have drawn everyone?
• Have you missed anyone?

At the garden centre: 1 and 2 (pages 41–42)

Processes: making decisions, recording, explaining, asking own questions, co-operating, looking for pattern, being systematic

These activities could usefully follow on from a visit to a Garden Centre or school vegetable patch. Encourage children to ask their own questions about the picture sheet and to say whether there are more or less of particular items. Encourage children to use numbers when describing what they can see. The Garden shopping price list can be used in informal play and role-play in the play area. Note that the prices can be masked and altered before copying to provide a flexible resource. Encourage discussion about the different costs of the items and the total cost for more than one item. Invite children to think about how they might choose to spend £10 at the garden centre.

SUGGESTED QUESTIONS:

• How many things can you see in this picture?
• Are there more… or fewer…?
• Talk to your partner about what you chose.
• What other questions could you ask?
• What if I bought a spade and a packet of seeds? How much would that cost?

In front of Fred (page 43)

Processes: looking for pattern, being systematic, predicting, comparing, explaining

The children should be given an opportunity to play with the cards and to spend time arranging them in queues and describing the situation by saying who is in front of Fred and who is behind. They can be encouraged to record different arrangements and talk about them to a partner. As an extension activity, ask the children to arrange the cards to match a description given by you, for example put them in a queue so that the cat, dog and frog are in front of Fred. When children have done this, look at different possible results, such as:

frog, cat, dog, Fred, rat, rabbit
frog, cat, dog, Fred, rabbit, rat,
frog, dog, cat, Fred, rat, rabbit
frog, dog, cat, Fred, rabbit, rat,
cat, frog, dog, Fred, rat, rabbit
cat, frog, dog, Fred, rabbit, rat, etc.
dog, cat, frog, Fred, rat, rabbit etc.

SUGGESTED QUESTIONS:

- How many different ways did you find?
- Who is in front of Fred here? Who is behind?
- How many animals are in front of Fred? How many behind?

Sari sorting (page 44)

Processes: looking for pattern, reasoning, explaining, comparing, making decisions

Here the children are required to recognise different patterns and to sort the cards into groups. Many will match the cards in pairs, but the children could also be asked to create two groups of cards with no two cards in a group the same, i.e. making two identical sets that each contain one of each pattern.

SUGGESTED QUESTIONS:

- Why have you decided to sort them like this?
- How many cards have you in each set?
- If you were going to choose one of the saris, which would it be? Why?
- Can you sort them another way?

Talk about, recognise and recreate simple patterns

Reasoning should go on in all areas of using and applying mathematics. This theme focuses on making deductions based on patterns, properties and relationships. The children should be encouraged to hear and develop the language and vocabulary of reasoning and to use logical steps when reasoning.

Pairs of socks (page 45)

Processes: looking for pattern, comparing

This activity can form a really nice display where a washing line with real socks is hung and children are asked to find pairs and count how many. Counting in twos can also be practised through this type of theme.

SUGGESTED QUESTIONS:

- How would you describe this pattern?
- Where is the one that matches this?
- How many socks altogether? How many pairs?

Leaf scribbles (page 46)

Processes: visualising, looking for pattern, comparing

This activity should be introduced practically in autumn, when children collect and use crayons to make prints from leaves and other flat shapes. As the children perform such practical activities they should be given opportunities to talk about and describe the shapes and patterns they are making, using their own vocabulary. Further questions can be asked to extend their descriptions, such as which leaf has five parts to it? Which leaf has only one pointed corner?

SUGGESTED QUESTIONS:

- What do you think the pattern for this leaf will look like?
- How many parts has this leaf?
- Is this curved or pointed?

Sand prints (page 47)

Processes: visualising, looking for pattern, comparing

The children should be given plenty of practical experience making prints in the sand tray using a variety of shapes and printing materials. As the children perform such practical activities they should be given opportunities to talk about and describe the shapes and patterns they are making, using their own vocabulary.

SUGGESTED QUESTIONS:

- What do you think made this print?
- Can you make some prints in the sand tray that are round/square?

Road signs (page 48)

Processes: making decisions, co-operating, looking for pattern, explaining

Encourage the children to work together and to both agree on which sign they would like to copy. They should then talk to each other about what is special about the sign, its shape, what it shows and perhaps what it might mean. The signs that the children make can be displayed in an outdoor area where play vehicles are used.

SUGGESTED QUESTIONS:

- Why did you choose this sign to copy?
- What is special about the shape of the sign?
- How are you going to draw the shape? What could you use to help you?

Fruit kebabs (page 49)

Processes: looking for pattern, predicting, testing ideas

This sheet works well as a follow-on activity to a practical session where the children use real pieces of fruit to make fruit kebabs. In the further extension activity, the children are invited to created their own fruit kebabs and justify their decisions about their choices. These could be drawn on cards for future use and to encourage discussion.

SUGGESTED QUESTIONS:

- What do you think will be the next piece of fruit in the pattern?
- Why did you choose to make this kebab?

Matt's patterns (page 50)

Processes: looking for pattern, being systematic, cooperation, explaining

This activity could be introduced in autumn with real items for the children to sort and arrange into patterns. The children could work in pairs or small groups to recreate and continue these patterns.

SUGGESTED QUESTIONS:

- What will be the next object in this line?
- Can you tell me about this pattern? What is special about it?

Kat's patterns (page 51)

Processes: looking for pattern, being systematic cooperation, explaining

For this activity, the children will need plastic shapes such as Logiblocks to recreate and continue these patterns. Encourage the children to describe any patterns they notice and to talk to a partner, suggesting reasons for the patterns if they can. The children should copy the patterns and make their lines even longer.

SUGGESTED QUESTIONS:

- What will be the next shape in this line?
- Can you tell me about this pattern? What is special about it?

Describe solutions to practical problems, drawing on experience, talking about their own ideas, methods and choices

The final theme is Communicating, including both oral and recorded communications. The children should be given opportunities to express their thinking, their reasoning and to communicate their findings to others and also to make personal records of their own. In lessons, the children should be encouraged to work with others, discussing decisions to be made, describing actions taken and conclusions made.

The chimp's challenge: 1 and 2 (pages 52–53)

Processes: reasoning, predicting, explaining, asking own questions

These problem-solving activities are those that encourage discussion of a problem, and consideration of how it could be solved. They can really begin to help children to think for themselves and to make suggestions and justify decisions. Enlarge one or both of the sheets onto A3 and stick onto the board. Invite the children to say what they think the Chimp's problem is and to suggest ways of solving it. Talk about problems with each of the suggested solutions, for example is it safe? What else could he do? How could he use things in the

picture to help him? As an extension activity, the children could draw their own problem pictures for others to talk about.

SUGGESTED QUESTIONS:

- What is the challenge?
- How could the chimp solve it?
- Is that a good idea? Why not?
- Can you think of a better idea?

The following activity sheets are designed for use in informal play areas and as resources for play activities to encourage numeracy talk and reasoning.

Fruit and veg stall (page 54)

Processes: co-operating, reasoning, making decisions, explaining, asking own questions

This activity sheet can be enlarged to A3 and stuck onto card or laminated for use in the play area. Cut out the price cards for the children to use in the play greengrocers where some of these items (plastic or real) are placed onto a table and the children place the price cards next to them. The children should take turns selling, choosing and paying for the items, including using coins and writing/giving receipts. It is not necessary for every transaction to be correct, but children should be given opportunities to informally use numbers and coins in this kind of way.

SUGGESTED QUESTIONS:

- How many oranges do you want?
- How much will that cost?
- How much change?
- Are there more bananas than carrots?

At the cinema (page 55)

Processes: co-operating, reasoning, making decisions, explaining, asking own questions

Although they may not be able to read and fully understand the information for themselves, model questions for them such as 'What time are you going to see the Spaceman film?' 'How long is it on for?' 'How much do you have to pay to get in?' and encourage the children to give 'play' answers which do not have to be correct.

SUGGESTED QUESTIONS:

- What time are you going to see the Trog film?
- How long is it on for?
- How much do you have to pay to get in?

Wall phone (page 56)

Processes: co-operating, reasoning, making decisions, explaining, asking own questions

This activity sheet should be placed at child height on the wall in one or more areas so that children can touch the numerals on the phone and pretend to make calls. These kind of informal activities that occur spontaneously help children understand that maths and numbers are part of everyday life and to appreciate their need to learn them. Observe the children's interactions and note who are able to correctly say and press numerals.

- Who are you going to phone?
- What is their number?
- Which keys do you need to press?
- Can you dial the number 3 6 5 8 for me?

Bus times (page 57)

Processes: co-operating, reasoning, making decisions, explaining, asking own questions

This sheet should be enlarged and placed on the wall in play areas inside or outside so that children can, during play, look at the timetable and decide which bus to wait for and catch. Informal activities of this kind that occur spontaneously, help the children to understand that maths and numbers are part of everyday life and to appreciate their need to learn them. Observe the children's interactions and note which of them are able to correctly read times and bus numbers.

Although the children may not be able to read and fully understand the information for themselves, model questions for them and encourage them to give 'play' answers which do not have to be correct.

SUGGESTED QUESTIONS:

- What is the number of the bus that you need?
- What time is it coming?
- When does it arrive at the shops?
- How long do you need to wait for?

Ticket master (page 58)

* *Processes: co-operating, reasoning, making decisions, explaining, asking own questions*

These tickets can be used informally in the play area, whether being bought at a kiosk or handed out to the bus driver etc. Model questions that help the children appreciate numeracy ideas in real life.

SUGGESTED QUESTIONS:

- How much does it cost for one child's ticket to the funfair?
- Have you got the correct coins?
- How much change?
- What will it cost for 2 tickets?
- Do you have enough tickets for the people here?

Rabbit maze and Mole maze (pages 59–60)

Processes: predicting, testing ideas, explaining, visualising

These two maze activities can be used to encourage the children to use positional vocabulary such as: up, down, across, under, left, right etc. in order to solve a problem.

SUGGESTED QUESTIONS:

- How can the rabbit/mole find its way out?
- Does he need to go up or down first?
- Which way should he go next?

Washing your hands: 1 and 2 (pages 61–62)

Processes: predicting, reasoning, making decisions,

being systematic

These sheets can be used in the classroom for sorting activities and for numeral recognition but should also be used to encourage healthy and clean routines in the toilets. Once the children have used and sorted these cards they could perhaps colour them and they could then be stuck in order in the toilets. Observe which children use the numerals to help them sort the cards and which focus on the hand-washing activity. The numerals could be masked before copying and the children asked to make predictions about the order of the cards before writing their own numerals on.

SUGGESTED QUESTIONS:

- Which card do you think comes first?
- Can you use the numbers to help you check?

A fishy tale: 1 and 2 (pages 63–64)

Processes: predicting, reasoning, making decisions, being systematic

These sheets can be used in the classroom for sorting activities, sequencing and for numeral recognition. Once the children have used and sorted these cards they could then be stuck in order on the wall. Observe which children use the numerals to help them sort the cards and which focus on the fishy tale. The numerals could be masked before copying and the children asked to make predictions about the order of the cards before writing their own numerals on.

SUGGESTED QUESTIONS:

- How did you decide which card came next?
- Now that you have put them in order, can you tell me the story of the fishy tale?

Using the CD-ROM

The PC CD-ROM included with this book contains an easy-to-use software program that allows you to print out pages from the book, to view them (e.g. on an interactive whiteboard) or to customise the activities to suit the needs of your pupils.

Getting started

It's easy to run the software. Simply insert the CD-ROM into your CD drive and the disk should autorun and launch the interface in your web browser.

If the disk does not autorun, open 'My Computer' and select the CD drive, then open the file 'start.html'.

Please note: this CD-ROM is designed for use on a PC. It will also run on most Apple Macintosh computers in Safari however, due to the differences between Mac and PC fonts, you may experience some unavoidable variations in the typography and page layouts of the activity sheets.

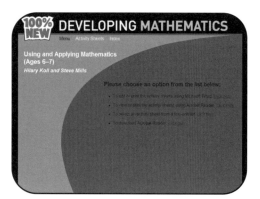

The Menu screen

Four options are available to you from the main menu screen.

The first option takes you to the Activity Sheets screen, where you can choose an activity sheet to edit or print out using Microsoft Word.

(If you do not have the Microsoft Office suite, you might like to consider using OpenOffice instead. This is a multi-platform and multi-lingual office suite, and an 'open-source' project. It is compatible with all other major office suites, and the product is free to download, use and distribute. The homepage for OpenOffice on the Internet is: www.openoffice.org.)

The second option on the main menu screen opens a PDF file of the entire book using Adobe Reader (see below). This format is ideal for printing out copies of the activity sheets or for displaying them, for example on an interactive whiteboard.

The third option allows you to choose a page to edit from a text-only list of the activity sheets, as an alternative to the graphical interface on the Activity Sheets screen.

Adobe Reader is free to download and to use. If it is not already installed on your computer, the fourth link takes you to the download page on the Adobe website.

You can also navigate directly to any of the three screens at any time by using the tabs at the top.

The Activity Sheets screen

This screen shows thumbnails of all the activity sheets in the book. Rolling the mouse over a thumbnail highlights the page number and also brings up a preview image of the page.

Click on the thumbnail to open a version of the page in Microsoft Word (or an equivalent software program, see above.) The full range of editing tools are available to you here to customise the page to suit the needs of your particular pupils. You can print out copies of the page or save a copy of your edited version onto your computer.

The Index screen

This is a text-only version of the Activity Sheets screen described above. Choose an activity sheet and click on the 'download' link to open a version of the page in Microsoft Word to edit or print out.

Technical support

If you have any questions regarding the *100% New Developing Literacy* or *Developing Mathematics* software, please email us at the address below. We will get back to you as quickly as possible.

educationalsales@acblack.com

Picnic planning: 1

- **Plan a picnic for** $\boxed{3}$ **bears.**
- **Decide what to take for them and how many of each you need.**

Teachers' note To be used in conjunction with the page 16. Ensure the children realise that they do not have to take every item shown here. They should choose whatever they like and can even choose other items not shown here. Encourage them to reason, such as 'Do you need to take the bowl if you are not taking anything that goes into a bowl, such as jelly?'

100% New Developing Mathematics Using and Applying Mathematics: Ages 4–5
© A & C BLACK

Picnic planning: 2

- **Draw all the things you plan to take to the picnic.**

Teachers' note Provide the children with page 15 to help them decide what to take. Ask related questions about their drawing such as 'Has each bear got the same things?' 'How many apples are being taken altogether?' 'Do you need three large bottles or can the bears share?' etc.

**100% New Developing Mathematics
Using and Applying Mathematics:
Ages 4–5**
© A & C BLACK

• **Cut out Sammy the starfish.**

• **Put Sammy so that he is touching:**

3 fish   1 fish   4 fish
2 fish   no fish

Teachers' note Children should cut out the square and use it to position Sammy in different places on the grid (only touching vertically or horizontally). Encourage the children to visualise and predict how many fish he touches in the different positions and to use trial and improvement strategies to find solutions. Discuss that there are several correct solutions for each.

100% New Developing Mathematics
Using and Applying Mathematics:
Ages 4–5
© A & C BLACK

17

• Cut out Sammy the starfish.

• Put Sammy so that he is touching:

2 fish and a crab   1 crab and 1 fish

2 crabs and a fish   2 fish

2 crabs   3 fish and a crab

Teachers' note Children cut out the square and use it to position Sammy in different places on the grid (only touching vertically or horizontally). Encourage the children to visualise and predict how many fish/crabs he touches in the different positions and to use trial and improvement strategies to find solutions. Discuss that there are several correct solutions for each.

100% New Developing Mathematics
Using and Applying Mathematics:
Ages 4–5
© A & C BLACK

Wonderful wellies

- **Guess whether there are enough boots for the feet.**
- **Tick** ✔ **or cross** ✗ **once you have checked.**

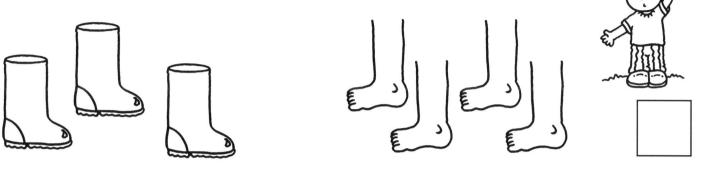

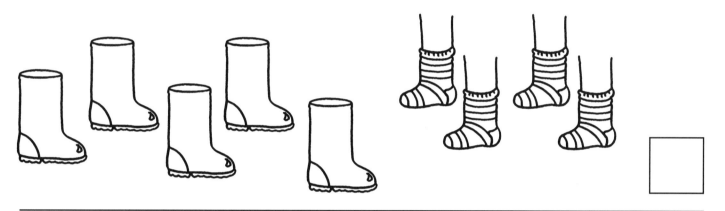

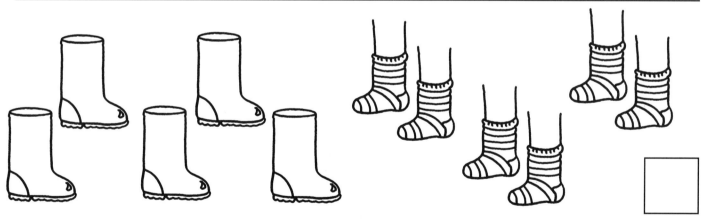

- **Now draw enough boots for these feet.**

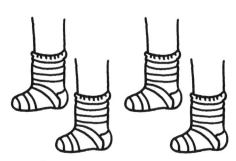

Teachers' note This sheet can be used as a follow on from the practical activity of looking at shoes or boots in the cloakroom or a play shoe shop. To help with counting, some children could be given cubes to place on each foot and boot.

100% New Developing Mathematics
Using and Applying Mathematics:
Ages 4–5
© A & C BLACK

Who sees who?

- **Put cubes on the shaded boxes to make walls.**

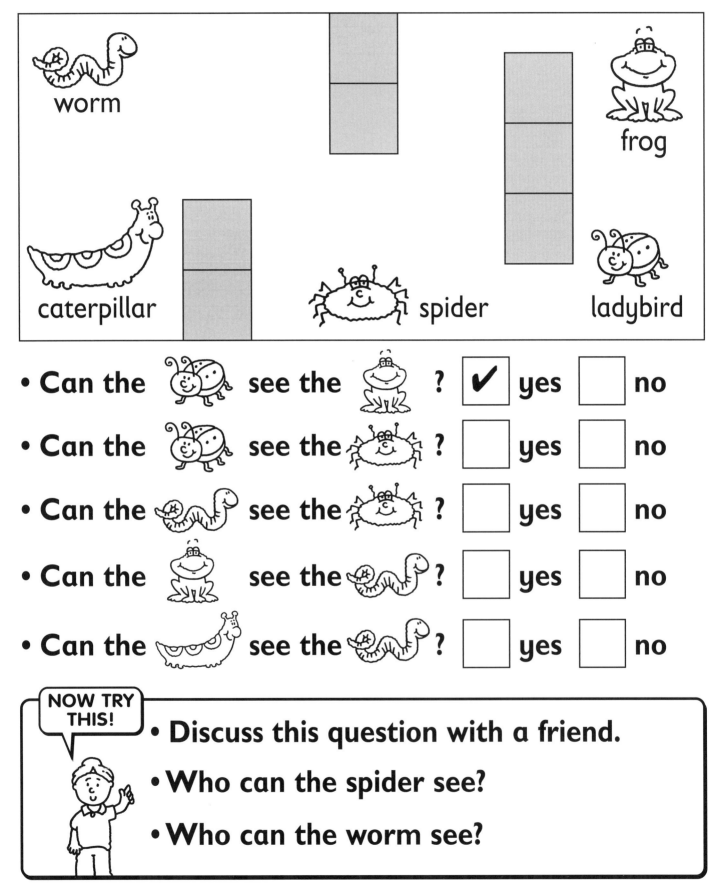

- Can the 🐞 see the 🐸 ? ✔ yes ☐ no
- Can the 🐞 see the 🕷 ? ☐ yes ☐ no
- Can the 🐛 see the 🕷 ? ☐ yes ☐ no
- Can the 🐸 see the 🐛 ? ☐ yes ☐ no
- Can the 🐛 see the 🐛 ? ☐ yes ☐ no

NOW TRY THIS!

- **Discuss this question with a friend.**
- **Who can the spider see?**
- **Who can the worm see?**

Teachers' note Ask the children to imagine that they are one of the creatures on the map and tell them that the cubes are tall walls. Could they see each of the other creatures? Ensure that children realise that the creatures can turn to look in all directions, e.g. the ladybird can turn to look at the frog. The children could also make their own 'maps' using small toys and cubes for walls and try a similar activity.

**100% New Developing Mathematics
Using and Applying Mathematics:
Ages 4–5
© A & C BLACK**

Wacky wigs: 1

- **Use only a red, blue or green pencil.**
- **Colour the wigs so that no two styles are the same.**

Teachers' note Watch to see how systematically the children colour each wig and remind them that they can only use red, blue or green and that each wig is only one colour. Draw attention to those children who systematically make the first column one colour, the second the next colour and so on. As an extension activity, provide the children with page 22.

**100% New Developing Mathematics
Using and Applying Mathematics:
Ages 4–5**
© A & C BLACK

Wacky wigs: 2

- **Use only a red, blue or green pencil.**
- **The halves of each wig are different colours.**
- **Colour the wigs so that no two wigs are the same.**

Teachers' note Watch to see how systematically children colour each wig and remind them that they can only use red, blue and green and that each wig is made from two colours. As an extension activity, ask the children to find how many different ways it is possible to colour wigs using two colours.

**100% New Developing Mathematics
Using and Applying Mathematics:
Ages 4–5
© A & C BLACK**

Colourful cotton reels

You need cotton reels in $\boxed{2}$ colours.

- **Build towers of** $\boxed{3}$ **reels. Make each** $\boxed{\text{different}}$.
- $\boxed{\text{Colour}}$ **below to show your towers.**

NOW TRY THIS!

- **Talk to a friend about how your towers are different.**

Teachers' note Give the children a set of cotton reels in two colours. For this activity, encourage them to make the towers different, for example red, red, blue and blue, red, blue. The children could make towers in just one colour, too. If cotton reels are not available, Multilink Cubes can be used. As a further extension, ask the children how many towers they can make with 3 different colours.

100% New Developing Mathematics
Using and Applying Mathematics:
Ages 4–5
© A & C BLACK

23

These two rugs make a cross.

• **Put the** same **number of counters on each rug.**

Teachers' note Give the children some counters and explain the activity. You could suggest that they try to place 4, 5 or 6 counters on each rug, and to find different solutions. The solutions could be recorded collectively, and further solutions found. Encourage the children to describe their thinking and any logical steps taken to find further solutions.

**100% New Developing Mathematics
Using and Applying Mathematics:
Ages 4–5**
© A & C BLACK

Hide the buns: 1

- **Put large counters on the buns to hide them, so that you can only see** $\boxed{3}$ **buns in each** $\boxed{\text{row}}$ **and** $\boxed{\text{column}}$ **.**

NOW TRY THIS!

- **Now try to hide the buns so that you can only see** $\boxed{2}$ **buns in each row and column.**

Teachers' note It is vital that the children understand what is meant by row and column for this activity. Provide them with counters and explain that they can cover any of the buns but you must still be able to see 3 buns in each row, going across, and 3 buns in each column, going down. Explain that there are many different possible solutions and give the children paper to record on.

**100% New Developing Mathematics
Using and Applying Mathematics:
Ages 4–5
© A & C BLACK**

Hide the buns: 2

• **Put large counters on the buns to hide them,** so that you can only see ┌3┐ buns in each ┌row┐ **and** ┌column┐.

NOW TRY THIS!

• **Now try to hide the buns so that you can only see ┌2┐ buns in each row and column.**

Teachers' note It is vital that the children understand what is meant by row and column for this activity. Provide them with counters and explain that they can cover any of the buns but you must still be able to see 3 buns in each row, going across, and 3 buns in each column, going down. Explain that there are many different possible solutions and give the children paper to record on.

100% New Developing Mathematics Using and Applying Mathematics: Ages 4–5
© A & C BLACK

Record on the clipboard

- **Fill in the chart to show how many.**

Teachers' note Put a number of the items shown on a table, or alter the sheet to show items that you have several of in the classroom. As this activity focuses on <u>beginning</u> to understand the importance of showing information clearly, it is not reasonable to expect all children to complete the table accurately. All marks show an awareness of the importance of recording to aid memory.

100% New Developing Mathematics
Using and Applying Mathematics:
Ages 4–5
© A & C BLACK

How many? 1

What are the children doing?
• How many children are doing each activity?

Teachers' note Ask the children to talk to a friend about what the children on this sheet are doing. Encourage them to say how many and ask questions such as: 'Are there more children skipping than playing in the sand tray? Are there fewer children looking at a book than are drawing? What are the largest group of children doing?' Give page 29 to children more confident with counting.

100% New Developing Mathematics Using and Applying Mathematics: Ages 4–5
© A & C BLACK

How many? 2

- **Cut out the cards.** Order **them.**
- **Write how many children are in each group.**

Teachers' note Use this sheet in conjunction with page 28.

100% New Developing Mathematics
Using and Applying Mathematics:
Ages 4–5
© A & C BLACK

Cube trail: 1

- **Cut out the cards.**
- **Put them in order with cubes on each square.**

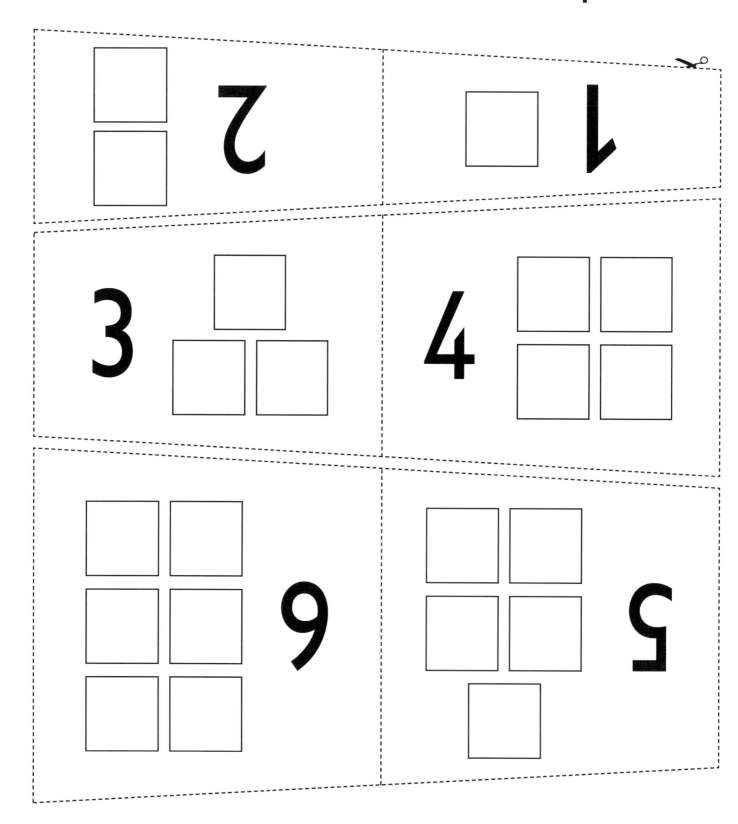

Teachers' note Provide the children with Multilink cubes to place on each card to show the numeral. Alternatively, the children could colour the squares and the number line could be stuck together and displayed on the wall. To be used in conjunction with page 31.

100% New Developing Mathematics
Using and Applying Mathematics:
Ages 4–5
© A & C BLACK

Cube trail: 2

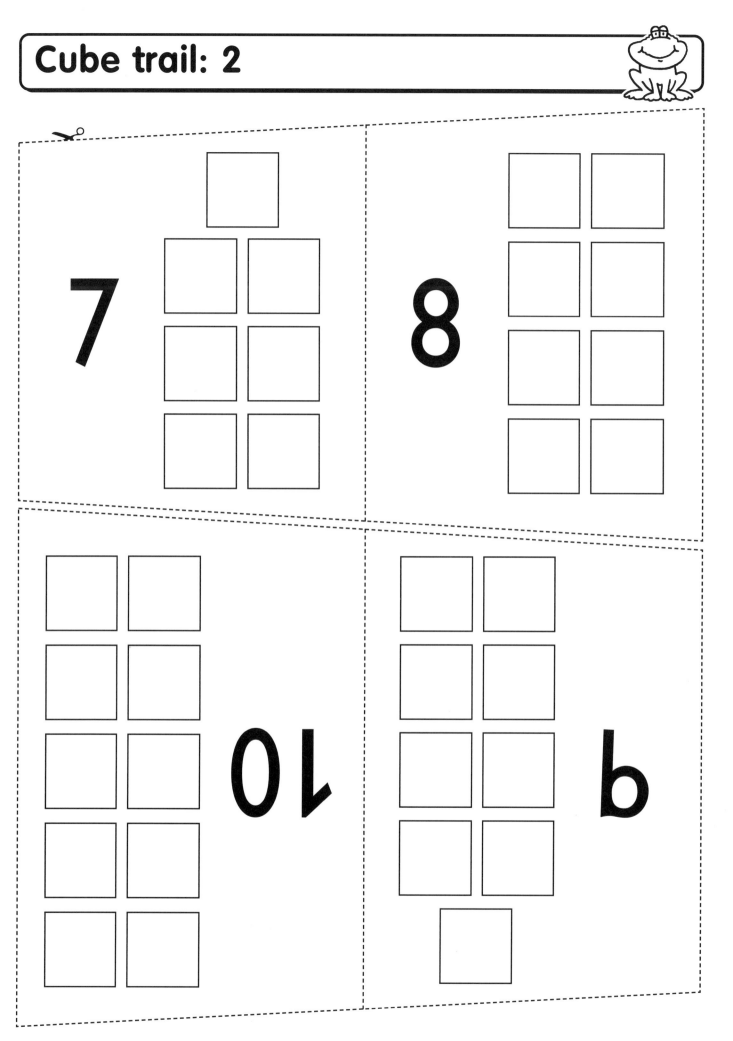

**100% New Developing Mathematics
Using and Applying Mathematics:
Ages 4–5**
© A & C BLACK

The zoo

- **Join each set of animals to a number to show how many.**

NOW TRY THIS!

- **Draw** 3 more **giraffes. How many?**

Teachers' note To introduce the zoo theme, say the following rhyme several times: 1, 2 Let's go to the zoo. 3, 4 Hear the tigers roar. 5, 6 Watch monkeys up to tricks. 7, 8 Feeding time is late. 9, 10 See the lions in their den. Encourage the children to join in. Then they can match the pictures with the numerals to show different sets of animals in the zoo.

**100% New Developing Mathematics
Using and Applying Mathematics:
Ages 4–5**
© A & C BLACK

Number puzzle

- **Cut along the dotted lines.**
- **Join the pieces together to make a number line.**

Teachers' note These pieces could be copied onto thin card, laminated, cut out and kept in a bag as a classroom resource. The numerals could also be coloured to make them more attractive.

100% New Developing Mathematics Using and Applying Mathematics: Ages 4–5 © A & C BLACK

Money magician

• **Draw the ⟨same⟩ number of coins in the other hand in each pair. Write how many altogether.**

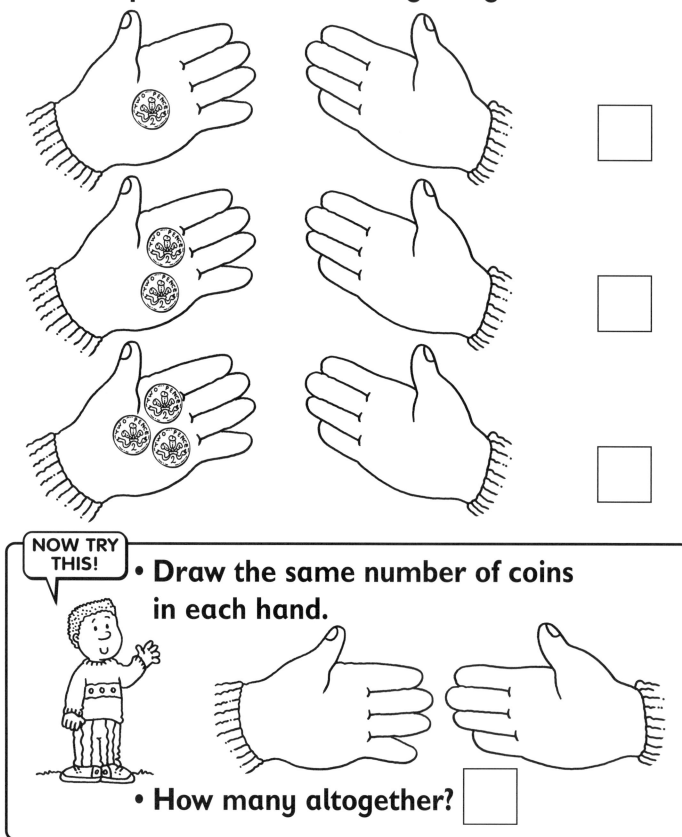

NOW TRY THIS!

• **Draw the same number of coins in each hand.**

• **How many altogether?**

Teachers' note Encourage the children to count the number of coins in both hands in each pair and to say any patterns they notice. Look at a number line and ask the children to find the numbers on it, i.e. the even numbers. Ask them to say whether it is possible to have an odd number of coins, if the same number is in each hand

100% New Developing Mathematics
Using and Applying Mathematics:
Ages 4–5
© A & C BLACK

Flower bugs

- **Cut out the pieces along the dotted lines.**
- **Join them together so that the number of bugs on each flower goes in the pattern 1, 2, 3, 4, 5, 6.**

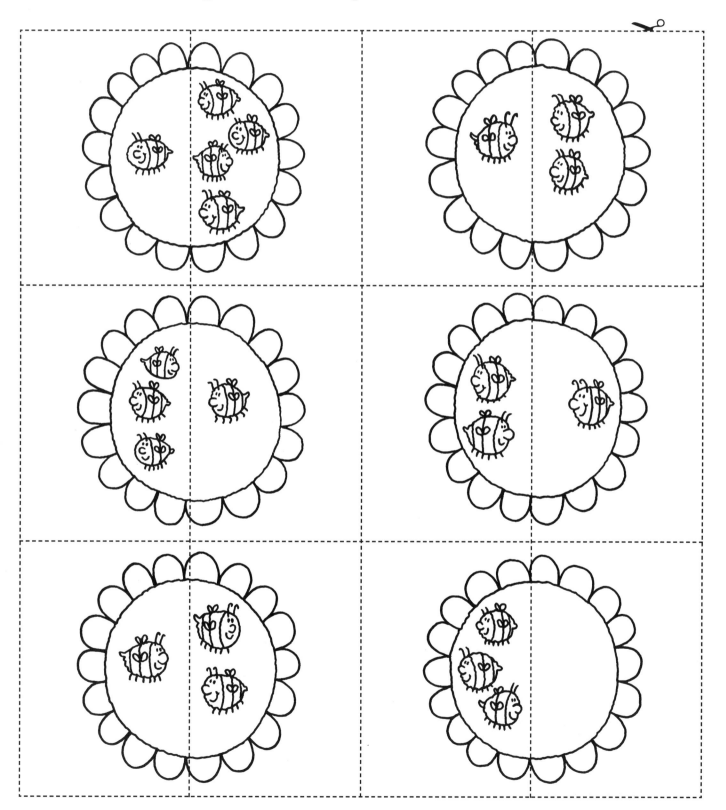

Teachers' note These pieces could be copied onto thin card, laminated, cut out and kept in a bag as a classroom resource. The flowers could also be coloured to make them more attractive. Ensure the children realise that they can rotate the halves of the flowerheads (although it is possible to find a solution without rotating the flowerheads).

**100% New Developing Mathematics
Using and Applying Mathematics:
Ages 4–5**
© A & C BLACK

35

Fishy friends

• Draw ▢more▢ fish so that there are ▢5▢ in each tank.

Teachers' note The number of fish in each tank could be adjusted according to ability. Children could be asked to describe each tank as a simple number sentence, for example 'One fish and four more fish makes five fish altogether'.

**100% New Developing Mathematics
Using and Applying Mathematics:
Ages 4–5**
© A & C BLACK

Underwater friends

- **Draw** more **creatures so that there are** 6 **on each rock.**

NOW TRY THIS!

- **Tell a friend how many creatures you have drawn on each rock.**

Teachers' note The number of creatures on each rock could be adjusted according to ability. Children could be asked to describe each rock as a simple number sentence, for example 'Two starfish and four more starfish makes six starfish altogether'.

100% New Developing Mathematics Using and Applying Mathematics: Ages 4–5
© A & C BLACK

Families

- **Cut out the cards.**
- **Sort the pictures into families.**

Work with a friend.

NOW TRY THIS!

- **Can you sort the cards in a different way?**

Teachers' note For this activity, encourage the children to sort not just into pictures of the same thing, but to think about whether there is an alternative way of sorting, such as grouping those items related to the numbers 2, 3 or 4. As a further extension activity, ask them to draw further cards to add to the sets.

**100% New Developing Mathematics
Using and Applying Mathematics:
Ages 4–5
© A & C BLACK**

Talking signs

- **Cut out the cards.**
- **Sort** the signs into groups.

Teachers' note The sheet could be copied onto A3 for larger signs. Provide one sheet per pair. Encourage the children to talk to each other about the signs and to decide how they would like to sort the signs into groups. Accept any ways of sorting, encouraging the children to explain their reasoning to others. The cards could be stuck onto different pieces of paper to show the sets.

100% New Developing Mathematics Using and Applying Mathematics: Ages 4–5 © A & C BLACK

Picture passports

- Draw yourself on a card and write your name.
- Make a card for each friend in your group.

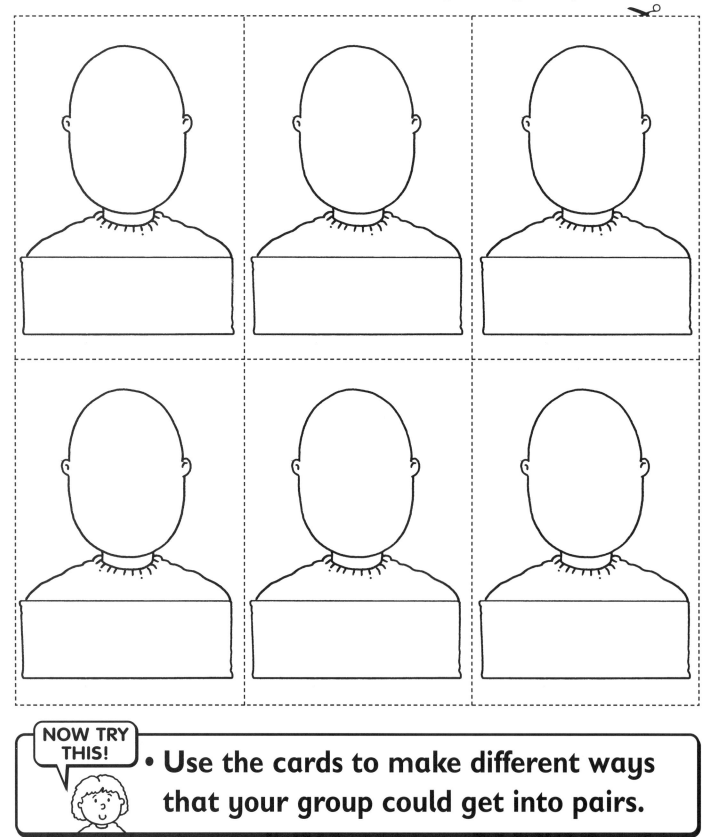

Teachers' note Organise the children into groups of six, ideally all seated around a table so that they can see each other. Encourage them to make a card for each person, including themselves. See page 10 for notes on how these cards can be used in a range of activities.

100% New Developing Mathematics
Using and Applying Mathematics:
Ages 4–5
© A & C BLACK

At the garden centre: 1

- **Talk to a friend about all the things you can see in this picture.**

NOW TRY THIS!

- **Use the words** more than **or** less than **to make up some** true statements **.**

Teachers' note Children must be encouraged to use numbers and to develop comparison vocabulary through informal and real-life situations, such as a visit to a garden centre. Encourage them to describe the picture to others in the class and to compare the number of items, for example: are there more trowels than spades? This sheet can be used in conjunction with page 42.

100% New Developing Mathematics
Using and Applying Mathematics:
Ages 4–5
© A & C BLACK

41

At the garden centre: 2

- **Decide which things you want to buy at the garden centre.**
- **How much will you have to pay?** £ _____

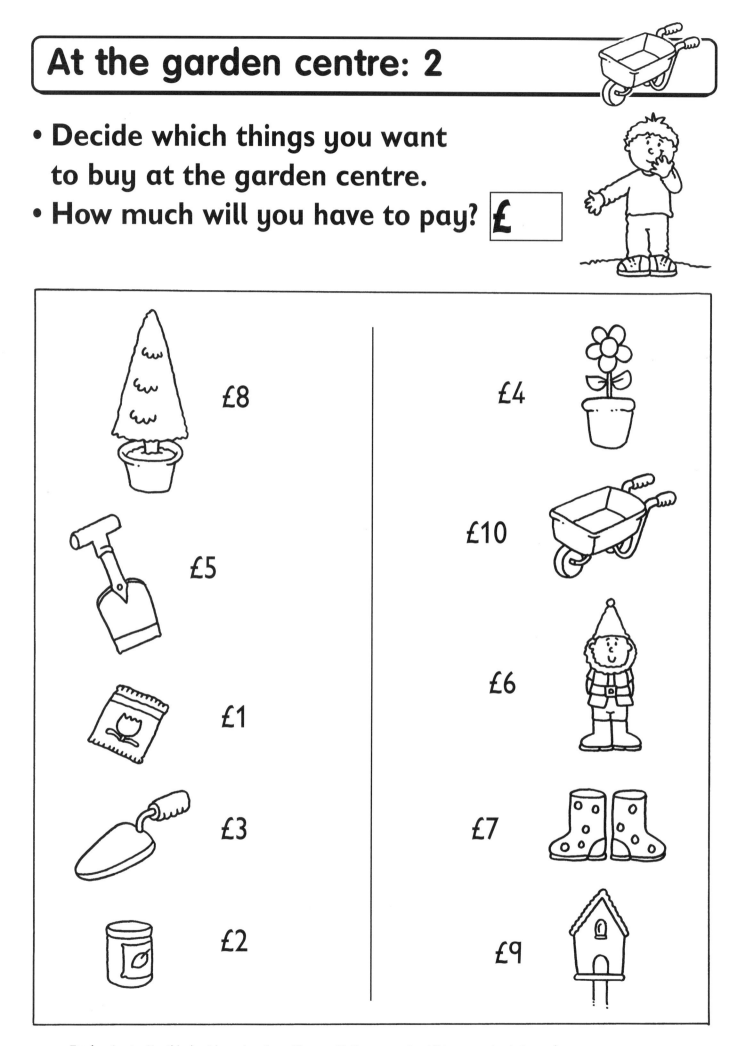

£8

£5

£1

£3

£2

£4

£10

£6

£7

£9

Teachers' note Use this sheet in conjunction with page 41. Encourage the children to make their own selections about what they might choose to buy, including multiple numbers of items if shown on page 41. Ask them to talk about coins they might use to pay. It is not essential that every calculation is correct, rather that children are talking about numbers and prices in real-life contexts.

100% New Developing Mathematics Using and Applying Mathematics: Ages 4–5 © A & C BLACK

In front of Fred

- **Cut out the cards and put them in a queue.**
- **Say which animals are** in front of **Fred and which are** behind .
- **Move the cards around and try again.**

Fred

Teachers' note This activity could follow on from a story such as *The Enormous Turnip* where people and animals follow each other in a line. Encourage the children to discuss different ways that the line could be arranged and to always describe who is in front and who is behind Fred. Collectively record solutions and encourage the children to describe their reasoning.

100% New Developing Mathematics
Using and Applying Mathematics:
Ages 4–5
© A & C BLACK

43

Sari sorting

- **Cut out the cards.** Sort **the saris into** groups **.**

Teachers' note Once the children have sorted the saris into groups they could use the cards to create different sequences of saris or they could rearrange the cards into two groups so that there is one of each kind of sari in each group.

100% New Developing Mathematics Using and Applying Mathematics: Ages 4–5
© A & C BLACK

Pairs of socks

- **Join the** matching **socks to make** pairs **.**

Teachers' note This activity could be used as an assessment sheet, following practical sorting of items in a washing basket. Encourage the children to describe similarities and differences between the different sock patterns shown and to design their own pairs of socks with other patterns.

**100% New Developing Mathematics
Using and Applying Mathematics:
Ages 4–5**
© A & C BLACK

Leaf scribbles

- Match each leaf with its scribble.

Teachers' note This activity can be introduced in a variety of ways. Children could collect and use real leaves or be given their own paper or plastic leaf shapes to use. They can then spray them or scribble over them with soft chalks or crayons to create a silhouette. Shapes and their silhouettes can be used to create a similar puzzle to the one on this page which can be used as a wall display.

100% New Developing Mathematics Using and Applying Mathematics: Ages 4–5
© A & C BLACK

Sand prints

- Match each sand print with the object that made it.

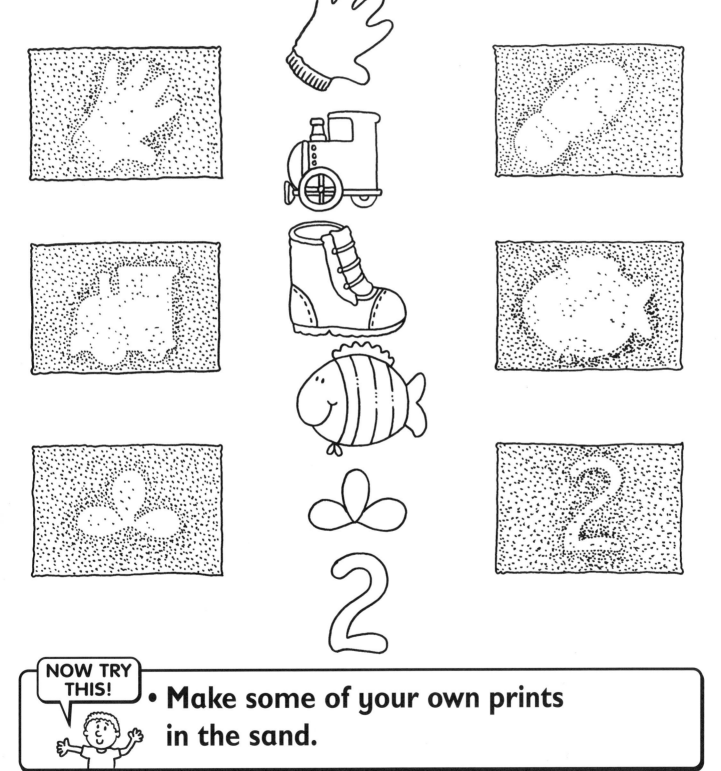

NOW TRY THIS!

- Make some of your own prints in the sand.

Teachers' note This sheet could be used as an assessment activity following practical experience of making prints in the sand tray. Ensure that children are given an opportunity to use a variety of shapes and printing materials and that they are encouraged to describe the prints they make. Discuss why the boot print is the shape that it is (it is the impression of the sole of the boot).

100% New Developing Mathematics
Using and Applying Mathematics:
Ages 4–5
© A & C BLACK

Road signs

- **Choose a sign and copy it.**
- **What is special about the sign?**

Work with a friend.

Teachers' note As an extension activity, ask the children whether, if their sign were cut in half, both sides would be the same or a reflection of each other.

**100% New Developing Mathematics
Using and Applying Mathematics:
Ages 4–5**
© A & C BLACK

Fruit kebabs

- ▢ Colour the pieces of fruit.
- **Use this key.**

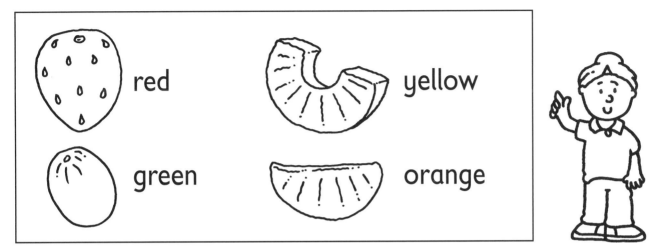

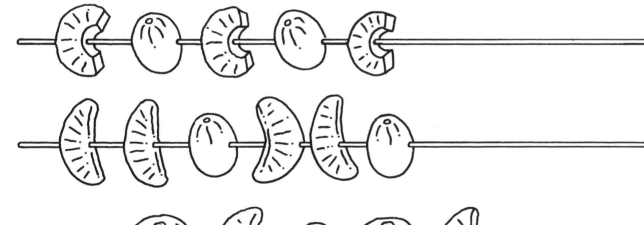

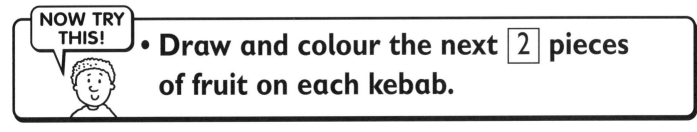

NOW TRY THIS!
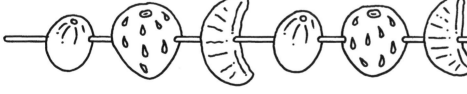
- **Draw and colour the next ▢2 pieces of fruit on each kebab.**

Teachers' note Provide the children with coloured pencils for this activity. As a further extension activity, ask the children to draw their own fruit kebab to make a pattern.

100% New Developing Mathematics Using and Applying Mathematics: Ages 4–5
© A & C BLACK

Matt's patterns

• Copy each of Matt's patterns. • Make your lines even longer than his.

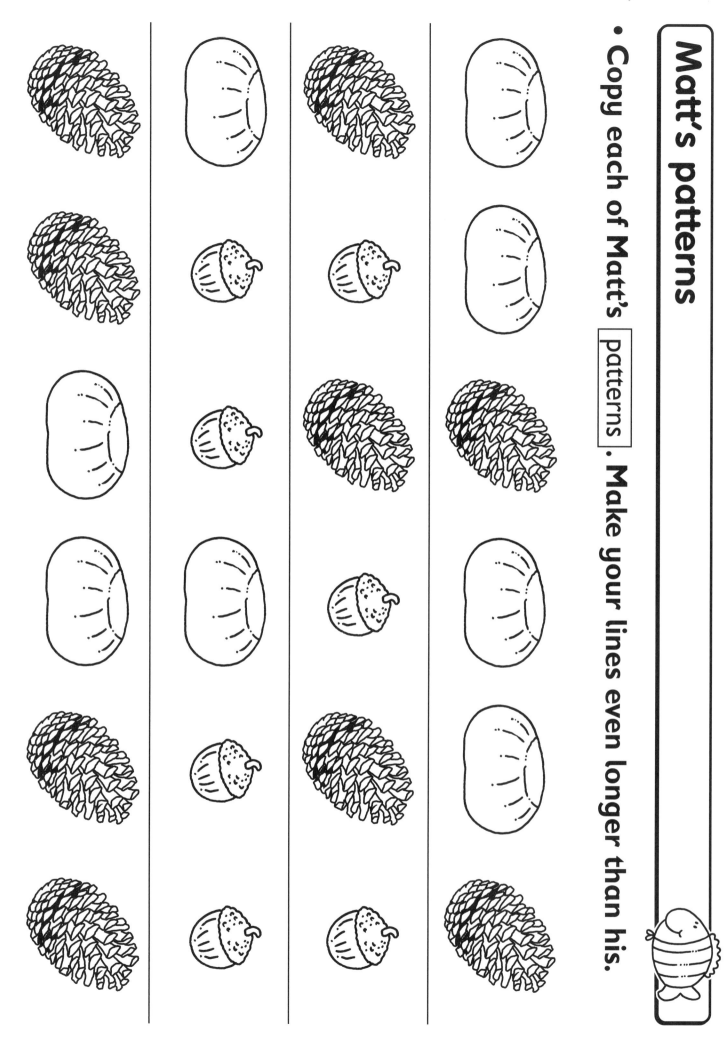

Teachers' note This is a useful autumn activity that can encourage the children to copy, continue and create their own patterns.

50

100% New Developing Mathematics
Using and Applying Mathematics:
Ages 4–5
© A & C BLACK

Kat's patterns

- Copy each of Kat's patterns . Make your lines even longer than hers.

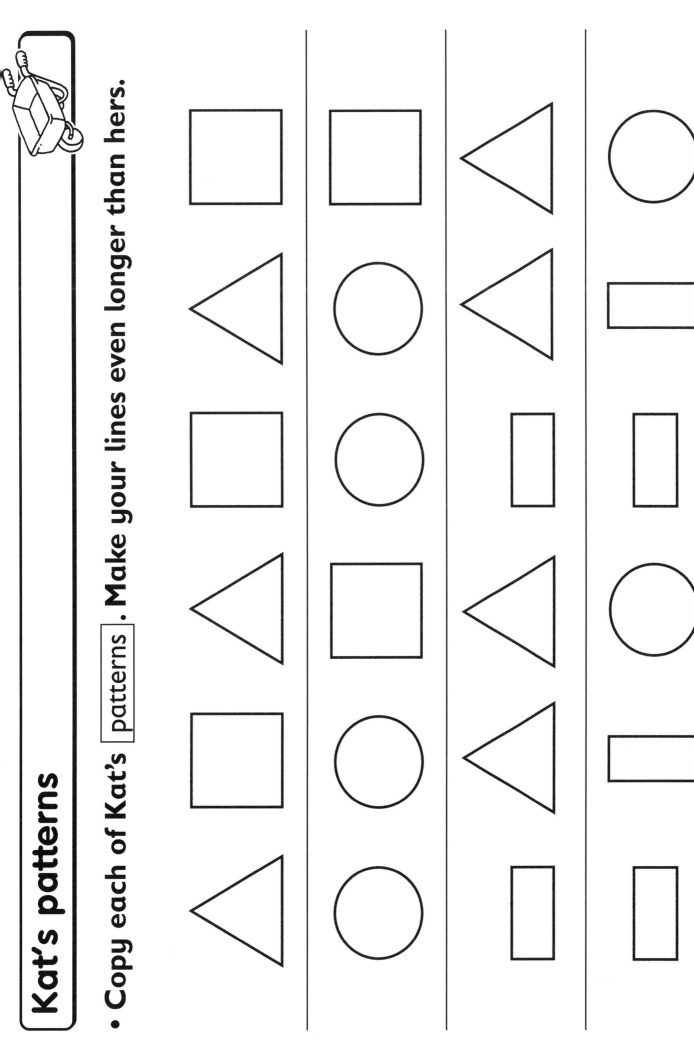

Teachers' note This is a useful activity that can encourage the children to copy, continue and create their own patterns.

100% New Developing Mathematics
Using and Applying Mathematics:
Ages 4–5
© A & C BLACK

The chimp's challenge: 1

• **What could the chimp do?**

Teachers' note Encourage the children to look at this picture and talk about what the chimp's problem might be. Ask them to talk to a friend about what they think the chimp should do to solve the problem. Then discuss all the ideas as a whole group and ask the children to draw a picture of the solution as they see it. Discuss any safety issues.

**100% New Developing Mathematics
Using and Applying Mathematics:
Ages 4–5**
© A & C BLACK

• **What could the chimp do?**

Teachers' note Encourage the children to look at this picture and talk about what the chimp's problem might be. Ask them to talk to a friend about what they think the chimp should do to solve the problem. Then discuss all the ideas as a whole group and ask the children to draw a picture of the solution as they see it. Discuss any safety issue.

100% New Developing Mathematics
Using and Applying Mathematics:
Ages 4–5
© A & C BLACK

Fruit and veg stall

• Cut out the price cards to use at the market stall.

6p each

5p each

4p each

3p each

2p each

1p each

Teachers' note Provide the children with some coins. Place some of these items (plastic or real) onto a table and encourage the children to place the price cards next to them and then take turns selling, choosing and paying for the items. Every transaction need not be correct, but this activity gives the children an opportunity to informally use numbers and coins in this kind of way.

100% New Developing Mathematics
Using and Applying Mathematics:
Ages 4–5
© A & C BLACK

At the cinema

Films now on...

£5

'Trog'

1 hour 30 minutes

Starts at

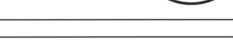

'Spaceman'

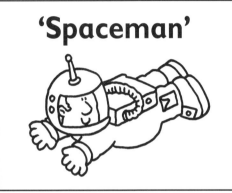

1 hour 30 minutes

Starts at

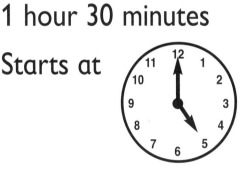

'The bees'

1 hour 15 minutes

Starts at

'My pal'

1 hour 30 minutes

2 hours 15 minutes

Starts at

Teachers' note This activity sheet can be enlarged to A3 and put on the wall in the role-play area to promote discussion. The children can talk to each other about films they would like to see, using the sheet as a stimulus. Vocabulary related to time and prices of tickets should be encouraged.

100% New Developing Mathematics Using and Applying Mathematics: Ages 4–5
© A & C BLACK

Wall phone

Teachers' note This phone can be used in a variety of ways, for example stick a copy of the activity sheet onto the wall of the classroom near a door or in the play area and encourage the children to key in different numbers to make telephone calls, or give the children a copy of the activity sheet and ask them to press the correct digit as you call out a telephone number.

100% New Developing Mathematics
Using and Applying Mathematics:
Ages 4–5
© A & C BLACK

Bus times

	School	**Shops**

Teachers' note This sheet can put on the wall in the role-play area. Encourage the children to ask each other questions about which bus they would like to take and what time it might come, for example, 'What time are you going to get on the bus?' 'What time does it reach the shops?' Encourage the children to give 'play' answers which do not have to be correct.

100% New Developing Mathematics
Using and Applying Mathematics:
Ages 4–5
© A & C BLACK

Ticket master

- ## Cut out the cards.

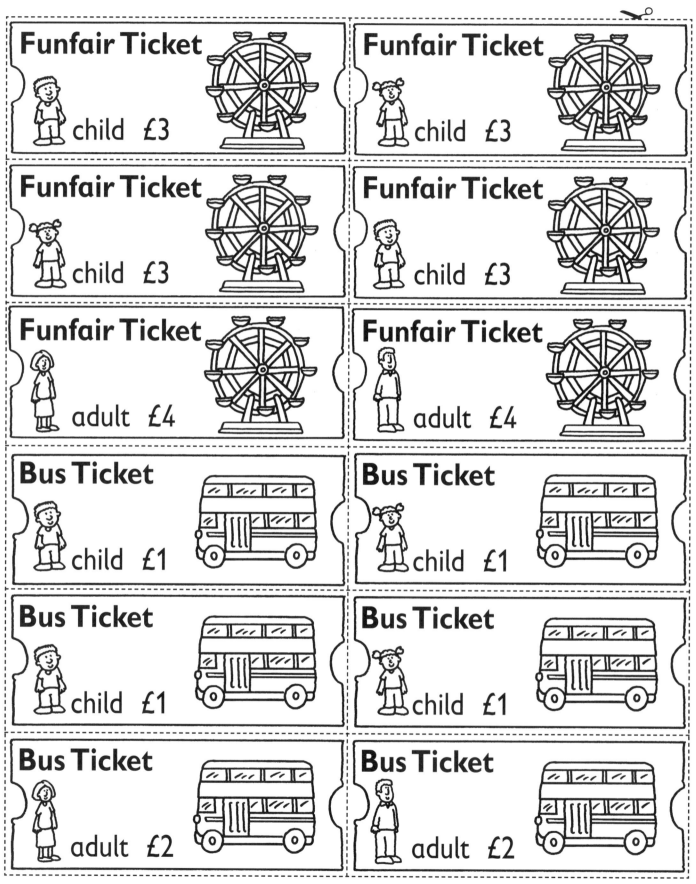

Funfair Ticket child £3

Funfair Ticket child £3

Funfair Ticket child £3

Funfair Ticket child £3

Funfair Ticket adult £4

Funfair Ticket adult £4

Bus Ticket child £1

Bus Ticket child £1

Bus Ticket child £1

Bus Ticket child £1

Bus Ticket adult £2

Bus Ticket adult £2

Teachers' note This activity sheet can be used as a role-play resource. Children can be given the tickets to use and give out. They should be encouraged to notice that they are for adults and children and for two different purposes. Provide the necessary coins.

100% New Developing Mathematics Using and Applying Mathematics: Ages 4–5
© A & C BLACK

Rabbit maze

• **Tell the rabbit how to get out of the** maze .

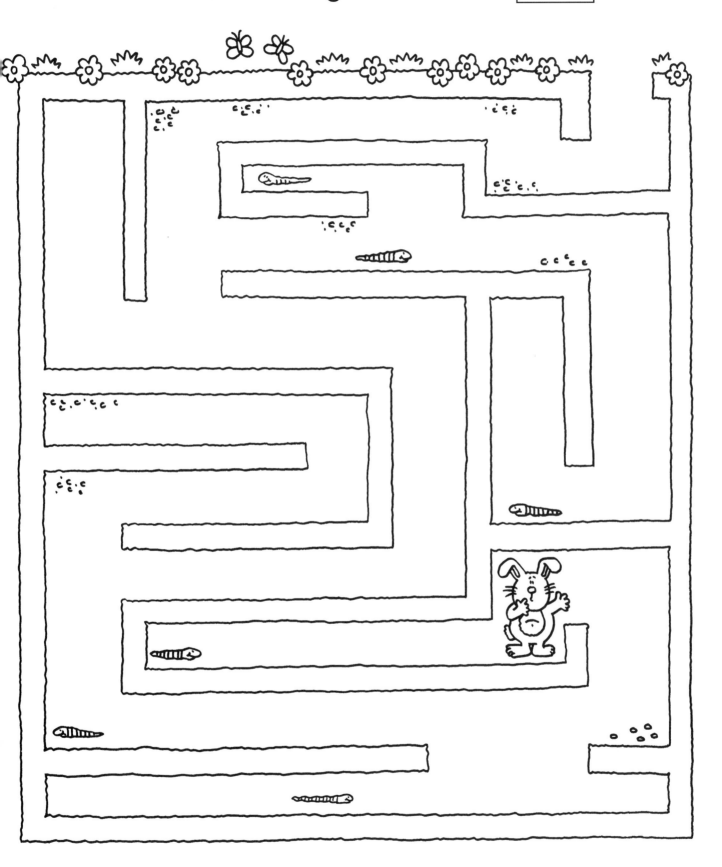

Teachers' note Encourage the children to talk to a friend about how the rabbit could get out of the maze. Encourage some children to tell the whole class, drawing attention to good positional vocabulary and clarity. The children could then be encouraged to draw the escape route for the rabbit.

100% New Developing Mathematics
Using and Applying Mathematics:
Ages 4–5
© A & C BLACK

Mole maze

- **Tell the mole how to get out of the** maze **.**

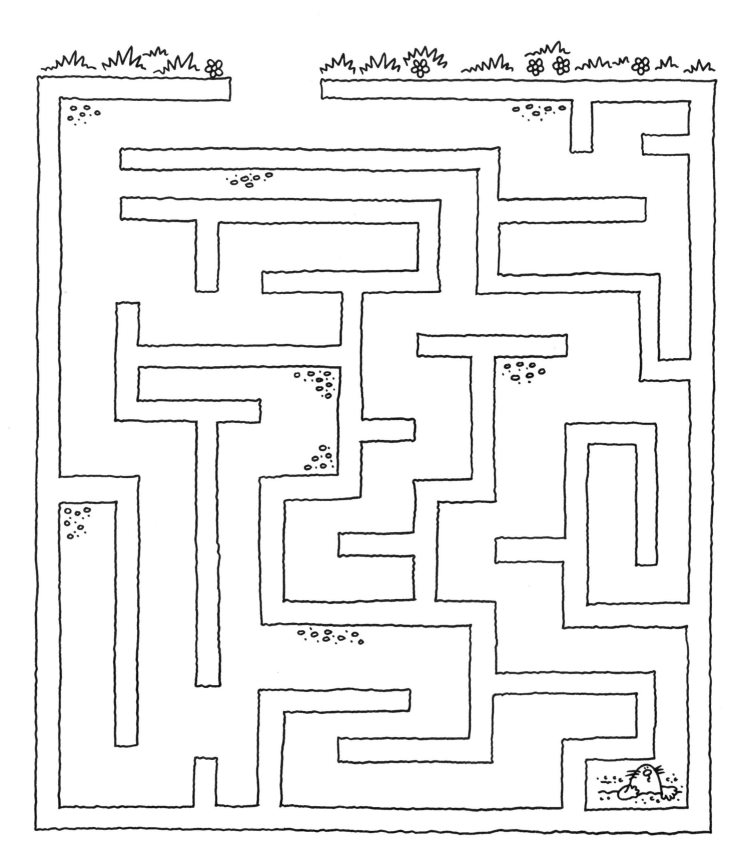

Teachers' note Encourage the children to talk to a friend about how the mole could get out of the maze. Encourage some children to tell the whole class, drawing attention to good positional vocabulary and clarity. Children could then be encouraged to draw the escape route for the mole.

**100% New Developing Mathematics
Using and Applying Mathematics:
Ages 4–5**
© A & C BLACK

Washing your hands: 1

- **You also need 'Washing your hands: 2'.**
- **Cut out the cards.**
- **Use the numbers to put them in order.**

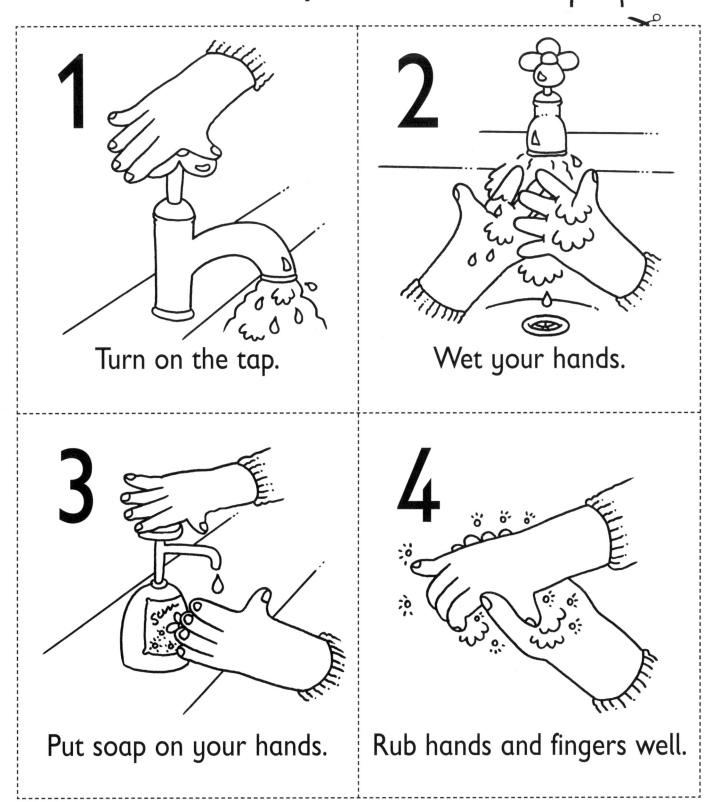

1 Turn on the tap.

2 Wet your hands.

3 Put soap on your hands.

4 Rub hands and fingers well.

Teachers' note This and the following sheet can be used in the classroom for sorting activities and for numeral recognition but should also be used to encourage healthy and clean routines in the toilets. Once the children have used and sorted these cards they could perhaps colour them and they could then be stuck in order in the toilets.

**100% New Developing Mathematics
Using and Applying Mathematics:
Ages 4–5**
© A & C BLACK

- **Cut out the cards.**
- **Use with 'Washing your hands: 1'.**

5 Rinse your hands.

6 Turn off the tap.

7 Dry with a paper towel.

8 Put the paper towel in the bin.

100% New Developing Mathematics
Using and Applying Mathematics:
Ages 4–5
© A & C BLACK

A fishy tale: 1

- **You also need 'A fishy tale: 2'.**
- **Cut out the cards.**
- **Put them in order.**

1 Drive to the shop.

2 Look around.

3 Buy lots of things.

4 Bring it all home.

Teachers' note This and the following sheet can be used in the classroom for sorting activities, sequencing and for numeral recognition. Once the children have used and sorted these cards they could then be stuck in order on the wall.

**100% New Developing Mathematics
Using and Applying Mathematics:
Ages 4–5**
© A & C BLACK

A fishy tale: 2

- **Cut out the cards.**
- **Use with 'A fishy tale: 1'.**

5 Fill tank with water.

6 Put plants in water.

7 Put fish in the tank.

8 Feed the fish.

Teachers' note Use in conjunction with page 63.

100% New Developing Mathematics Using and Applying Mathematics: Ages 4–5
© A & C BLACK